1969

This book may be kept

abc's
of
SHORT-WAVE LISTENING

by LEN BUCKWALTER

 HOWARD W. SAMS & CO., INC.
THE BOBBS-MERRILL CO., INC.
INDIANAPOLIS · KANSAS CITY · NEW YORK

SECOND EDITION

FOURTH PRINTING—1969

Library of Congress Catalog Card Number: 67-19017

PREFACE

Short-wave radio has given rise to a breed of armchair adventurers who "roam" the world with a twist of the dial on their receivers. Few events are barred from the ears of the avid listener—from the anxious distress call of a sinking ship to the weird beeping from an orbiting satellite.

But there is much more than just excitement on the short-wave bands; the busy wavelengths abound in programs of entertainment and educational value. Many are transmitted in English from such distant points as Tokyo, London, Moscow, Paris, Berlin, and Manila. All these and many more fascinating programs are beamed directly to you, the short-wave listener.

The key to this wonderful new world is yours for the asking—just some modest equipment and the desire to discover the world from the comfort of your own home.

LEN BUCKWALTER

Contents

Chapter 1

Short-Wave Listening

Three faint pulses of sound announced the birth of short-wave radio in 1901. Encamped on Signal Hill in the southeastern corner of Canada, Guglielmo Marconi strained to hear the first trans-Atlantic radio signals from England. During this historic moment, Marconi demonstrated to the world that radio was not merely a laboratory curiosity capable of limited range, but rather a revolutionary new medium for global communications.

Although Marconi's feat excited people everywhere, it literally rocked the scientific world. Distinguished physicists were virtually unanimous in their reaction: "Mathematically impossible," they said. It was generally believed that radio, like light, travelled in perfectly straight lines. Thus, it could not curve over the earth's surface to form a link between two distant points. Scientific reasoning suggested that a signal from England would shoot off into space and never reach Canada. The problem was further aggravated by the fact that no one ventured a plausible explanation for the strange behavior of radio waves in Marconi's experiment.

Obviously, the scientists were wrong, as Marconi continued to conquer great distances with his primitive equipment. The first inkling of an explanation stirred in 1902. While aboard the ocean liner Philadelphia, Marconi observed that messages could be received successfully from distances of 700 miles by day and 2,000 miles at night. In some way, radio waves were being affected by the earth's atmosphere. Stimulated by this steady build-up of evidence, theories began to sprout. Both A.E. Kennelly and O. Heaviside, while working independently of each other, soon came up with the idea of an electrical region high in the earth's atmosphere that can act like a mirror to radio waves. Instead of heading into space, radio-wave energy can be reflected back to the earth where it can be received by a distant station. As a tribute to the correctness of the idea, the region was designated the Kennelly-Heaviside layer. Today it is more commonly called the *ionosphere*. The special behavior of this electrified region is largely responsible for the vast field of short-wave radio.

By 1925, careful measurements of the ionosphere had been taken. Through a process of beaming brief radio pulses to the upper layers of the atmosphere, returning echoes yield much information about the nature of the ionosphere. Scientists soon perceived the over-all picture of a huge umbrella-like layer over much of the earth. This layer invisibly ebbed and flowed with the passing days and seasons. They noted that certain radio frequencies passed through unobstructed, while others reflected at various angles. Once the secrets of the ionosphere were laid bare, the next 50 years witnessed tremendous development in the field of long-distance communications. Even today rockets and satellites probe the region to add to the existing store of information.

Thus, the field of short-wave radio was born. And with it was ushered in the fascinating hobby of short-wave listening (Fig. 1-1). As an increasing number of stations took to the air in the 1920's, people thrilled to sounds which they knew had originated many miles away. For some, it provided their first contact with people, places, and events

Fig. 1-1. The short-wave fan finds listening interesting day or night.

far beyond the area in which they lived. Others took to short-wave listening to enjoy the technical challenge of building equipment capable of receiving distant signals.

The hobby of short-wave listening is enjoyed today with all the excitement discovered by the "old timers" several generations ago. It is a field which constantly grows, offering the SWL'er an increasing number of ways in which he can enjoy his hobby within the comforts of his own home. Early equipment with its tricky *cat's whisker* adjustments, or costly battery, has been replaced by the infinitely more sensitive superhet receiver. In addition, the hobbyist no longer has to operate during late-evening hours to pick up isolated stations. Throughout the day or night, the wide coverage of the SW receiver brings in distant signals at many points on the dial.

In contrast to bygone days, there are now over 3,000 stations broadcasting to the world's short-wave listeners. Operating at high power, they fill the wavelengths with programs of every conceivable type. Consider the British Broadcasting Corporation (BBC), whose "External Programme Operations" (Fig. 1-2) began regular service to the world in 1932. Operating 37 powerful transmitters in England, the BBC output reaches the staggering figure of over 500 hours per week! Through a system of eight networks, programs are broadcast in forty-one different languages. Thousands of people the world over tune to the BBC, especially to hear the newscasts, which are noted for their ac-

Courtesy British Broadcasting Corporation.

Fig. 1-2. "Dateline London" is one of the many hundreds of programs broadcast by BBC, one of the world's leading short-wave stations. Shown here is host Lee Hamilton and Julie Andrews.

curacy and impartiality. They are delivered at the rate of 1,000 per week on a global basis. The BBC schedule also includes many programs of cultural and educational value.

The strong voice of the French Broadcasting System also beams programs to the short-wave listener (Fig. 1-3). A huge half-million watt facility at Allouis, France transmits

Courtesy Radiodiffusion-Télévision Francaise.

Fig. 1-3. Powerful short-wave station in France presents language course: "French by Radio."

regularly in French and English to the North-American continent. Also, Radio Moscow delivers a considerable number of newscasts and reports of industrial and scientific progress —all intended to propagandize the American listener with the Soviet point of view.

Whatever your interest, you'll probably find it covered on the short-wave bands; a talk on West Indian wrestling, a lesson in Japanese with Dr. Toru Matsumoto (Fig. 1-4), or perhaps jazz played Dutch style. There's opera, folk music, symphonic works, popular tunes and talks on stamp

11

collecting and literature. Radio Nigeria offers a community sing. Radio Manila sounds the "Call of the Orient," and Radio Japan conducts a guided tour through points of interest in the Japanese islands. The bands are literally filled with programs of education and information (Fig. 1-5), and there is no language barrier. A large portion of the broadcasts from world capitals are in English; particularly if they are beamed to the United States. Of course, if you are learning a foreign language, a short-wave receiver affords

Courtesy Nippon Hoso Kyokai.

Fig. 1-4. "Let's Speak Japanese" is beamed to America twice a week from Tokyo for English-speaking audience.

a marvelous pronounciation guide. Just listen to the country of your choice.

Short-wave listening is not restricted to the outpouring of international broadcast stations. Dotted throughout the bands is a myriad of communications services that often afford exciting listening (Fig. 1-6). Hundreds of SWL'ers heard the dramatic distress and rescue operations the night the Andrea Doria sank after a collision at sea. The marine frequencies also bring the chatter of tugboat captains or reports of fishing conditions from commercial and pleasure boats. Aviation enthusiasts can eavesdrop on airport control towers or hear the voices of pilots as they fly over the ocean. Many SW sets can receive police, fire, and civil defense traffic. The "rag chewing" of radio hams (Fig. 1-7) situated all over the world can be relied on for an unending source of worthwhile technical and general comments.

To the rich and varied content of short-wave listening is added yet another exciting dimension—the realm of outer space. SWL'ers have discovered that over and beyond the earth's horizon, the void is being filled with radio signals from satellites and manned space capsules. Whether it's the

Courtesy Radio Corporation of America Internationale.

Fig. 1-5. Performers in Karachi before the microphones of Radio Pakistan.

13

"beep-beep" of a telemetry signal from a space probe, or the voice of an astronaut in orbit, many of these signals can be heard by the SWL'er at home on standard equipment. In fact, a considerable body of valuable tracking information has been funnelled to the scientist through monitoring reports sent by SWL operators.

Courtesy American Red Cross.

Fig. 1-6. Scene of disaster brings two-way mobile radios which can be picked up by the SWL'er.

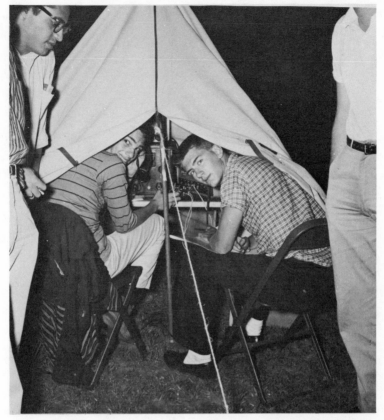

Courtesy QST Magazine.

Fig. 1-7. The SWL'er can tune in on hundreds of ham stations, like this one, and listen to conversations from around the world.

These are just samples of the exciting rewards waiting to be discovered on the short-wave bands. Acquiring them is not difficult; there is no license requirement, electronic skill, or prohibitively expensive equipment needed. But, as in any engaging and lasting hobby, enjoyment grows with experience and knowledge. For the short-wave listener, this means familiarity with the behavior of short waves, his receiver, antennas, tuning, program schedules, and a variety of other practical details, which we will explore next.

15

Chapter 2

The Short-Wave Signal

No one has ever seen a short-wave signal! It is an invisible field of energy which travels at the speed of light as it carries a program from the antenna of a station (Fig. 2-1) to the short-wave set. Yet, it is possible to describe and predict much about its behavior. In the process, many terms that comprise the working vocabulary of the SWL'er begin to take on meaning. Words such as *wavelength, frequency, meter,* and even *short wave* itself can be understood and put to practical use. Let's begin by examining some of the most basic features of radio waves; the raw material which makes up the very fabric of a short-wave signal.

The forces which produce a radio wave originate in the heart of the transmitter at the sending station. There, electrical currents are made to surge back and forth at extremely high speeds. As they progress through various stages in the transmitter, these alternating currents are boosted in power (Fig. 2-2) and finally applied to the transmitting tower. It is in this area that currents give rise to

17

the actual radio wave.—the field of energy which travels outward from the tower.

A picture of the wave, as shown in Fig. 2-3, helps to explain some common terms used in short-wave listening. The curving line represents the strength and direction at a given instant. Since the wave is generated by electrical currents

Courtesy Radiodiffusion-Télévision Francaise.

Fig. 2-1. Transmitting facility of French broadcasting system at Allouis, France.

Fig. 2-2. Final stage of station shown in Fig. 2-1 produces 500 kilowatts of power.

19

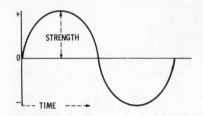

Fig. 2-3. One cycle of a wave.

which surge along the length of the antenna, the wave shows similar variations. If the starting point is considered to be at the left, it is seen that the line starts from the zero point, rises, then returns to zero. This represents the part of the wave which is created when currents flow in one direction in the tower. As the same current reverses, so does the wave direction. This is shown by the line falling below the zero point. An excellent way to visualize the action is to compare it with the dropping of a pebble into a pond. Ripples are created which move in ever-widening circles. Each wave of water has a peak, or high point, which is immediately followed by a dip or trough. These peaks and dips correspond to the positive and negative movements of the radio energy, as illustrated in Fig. 2-3.

Let's stop the transmitter at this point to examine the waveform more closely. What has been shown in Fig. 2-3 is the radio wave going through one complete *cycle*. The number of these cycles occurring each second determines the *frequency* of the wave. A station in the standard broadcast band, for example, might operate on an assigned frequency of 1,000,000 cycles per second. Since we are dealing with millions of cycles though, it is simpler to abbreviate the figure to 1,000 kc*. The abbreviation *kc* means *kilocycles*, or one thousand cycles. But frequencies in the short-wave

---

*To honor Heinrich Hertz, 19th century Austrian physicist who conducted early experiments with radio waves, the term "cycles per second" has been supplanted by "hertz" by much of the electronics industry. Thus, cycles per second becomes hertz (abbreviated Hz); kilocycles becomes kilohertz (kHz); and megacycles becomes megahertz (MHz). However, in this book, we use the terms cycles, kilocycles (kc), and megacycles (mc).

bands often run considerably higher, and the abbreviation mc (megacycle) is often applied. Since it stands for 1,000,000 cycles, the station frequency mentioned above could also be written as 1 mc.

The ability to convert kc to mc is especially important for reading short-wave schedules. Station frequencies are given in either form. The dial of the SW receiver may be scaled with both systems. The rules are simple: anytime you wish to convert kc to mc, move the decimal point three places to the left (for example, 2,300 kc = 2.3 mc). Reversing the system, 6.2 mc becomes 6,200 kc.

Another means of identifying a radio wave is in terms of wavelength. This is the distance between one cycle and the next, as the waves radiate from the transmitting antenna. In comparing wavelength with the pebble and water-wave example, it is equivalent to the number of inches between each peak, or crest. With radio energy, however, the standard is the *meter* (one meter = 39.37 inches). That wavelength will always vary with station frequency, as illustrated by Fig. 2-4.

Let's assume that the frequency of the wave in Fig. 2-4A is 15 mc (15 million individual cycles occurring each second). Wavelength for this is measured between points A and B. But suppose that the number of cycles per second were doubled (to 30 mc), as in Fig. 2-4B. The important difference to observe is that a 30-mc wave has two cycles for every one of the 15-mc signal. In effect, the higher the frequency, the shorter the wavelength.

It is valuable to the short-wave listener to know how to convert frequency to wavelength. Although a specific station is always located on the dial by means of its exact frequency in kc or mc, quite often wavelength (in meters) is used for general discussion. For example, the SWL'er might read reports about conditions on the 31-meter band. This is more convenient than singling out particular frequencies within that band which lies between 9,200 kc and 9,700 kc. The characteristics of each of these close-spaced frequencies is uniformly the same.

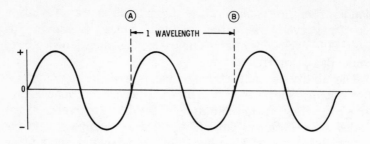

(A) Fundamental frequency.

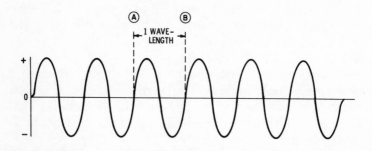

(B) Frequency doubled.

Fig. 2-4. Doubling the frequency cuts the wavelength in half.

The formula for converting frequency to meters is:

$$\text{Wavelength (in meters)} = \frac{300{,}000{,}000}{\text{freq. (in cycles per second)}}$$

The 300,000,000 figure is always the same; it is the constant speed of all radio waves. (300,000,000 meters per second is the speed of light.) If you are dealing with kc or mc, the figure must be changed to cycles per second. As an example, what is the wavelength of a station operating on 30 mc?

$$\text{Wavelength} = \frac{300{,}000{,}000}{30{,}000{,}000}$$

$$\text{Wavelength} = \frac{30 \ (mc)}{3 \ (mc)}$$

$$\text{Wavelength} = 10 \text{ meters}$$

As familiarity with the SW bands increases, you'll find only occasional use for the formula. The major bands are soon memorized in terms of wavelength versus frequency. However, there is a mental shortcut which may be used. If one band is known, it's simple to approximate several others. Anytime the frequency is cut in half, wavelength is doubled. In the above example, 30 mc is equal to 10 meters; and you would be correct in assuming 15 mc is equal to 20 meters.

There is one instance when the formula is especially important: the design of special antennas which the SWL'er might wish to construct for exclusive reception on a particular band. As discussed in a later chapter, the formula yields the exact length of wire needed for the construction of such an antenna.

Armed with the fundamental terms used in short wave, we can now consider the radio spectrum as a whole. It is a region which commences at the very-low frequency of approximately 10 kc and extends upward and beyond 30,000 mc. Other types of energy border the radio spectrum, but they are characterized by different properties. Light and X rays, for example, populate the frequencies above the radio region. All short-wave listening is done on one or more

Table 2-1. The radio spectrum.

MAJOR DIVISIONS	FREQUENCY RANGES
VLF=Very Low Frequency	10 KC-30 KC
LF=Low Frequency	30 KC-300 KC
MF=Medium Frequency	300 KC-3,000 KC
HF*=High Frequency	3 MC-30 MC
VHF=Very High Frequency	30 MC-300 MC
UHF=Ultrahigh Frequency	300 MC-3,000 MC
SHF=Superhigh Frequency	3,000 MC-30,000 MC
*Most SW listening is done in this part of the spectrum.	

23

of the seven major divisions shown in Table 2-1. By far the most popular classification is in the high-frequency (HF) range, from 3-30 mc. As you will see in the next chapter, this is the area for long-distance broadcasting. To a lesser extent, there is activity of interest on the medium (MF) and very high frequencies (VHF).

Finally, consider the definition of the word *short wave*. It may be a surprise to many, but the word itself is a living antique and survives by weight of tradition. It gives only a general description of a vague area in today's complex spectrum. In radio's earlier day, short wave meant anything above the standard broadcast band in the MF region. Since these waves were known to be high in frequency, it followed that wavelengths were short. Thus, the term short wave evolved. But a short-wave listener today might actually be an LF listener, if he has equipment which can tune to stations in the 200-kc region. Wavelengths in this band are much longer than standard broadcast. But, in spite of its technical limitation, short-wave listening is a durable and descriptive term for operations anywhere outside the standard bands of AM, FM and TV.

Chapter 3

The Ionosphere

Without the ionosphere most short-wave listening would cease. It is this electrified layer of air extending about 60 to 250 miles above the earth's surface which gives rise to *skip*. It is this skip pathway that carries radio signals between continents, overseas, and indeed, around the world. The ionosphere is not firmly fixed in place; constant shifts in position and thickness have a profound effect on radio waves. These and other factors determine whether a particular station can be received at a given time. For this reason, some knowledge of the ionosphere is of significant value to the short-wave listener.

The formation of the ionosphere is generally believed to be a result of the sun's action on the upper atmosphere. As huge amounts of ultraviolet radiation bombard gas molecules, an ionizing effect occurs; molecules are broken down into charged particles. The amount of ionization differs at varying heights; and a series of layers, which comprise the ionosphere as a whole, are created.

Since the sun has a direct effect on the ionosphere, the individual ionospheric layers are subject to great variation as the earth rotates. When the sun sets in a particular region, a reduction in ultraviolet radiation causes the ionosphere to thin out and recede to greater heights. Seasons also alter the amount of radiation; they similarily influence the structure of the ionosphere, but over a longer period of time. Another major effect is caused by the mysterious sunspots which appear to cross the face of the sun in varying groups. When the average number of sunspots goes up, ultraviolet radiation rises with it. Thus, the most definite thing to be stated about radio conditions is that they change—hourly, with the seasons, and according to the sunspot cycle.

A basic view of ionospheric propagation is shown in Fig. 3-1. Depending on frequency, a radio wave may follow one of three principal paths as it travels away from the transmitting station (point A). For the lower end of the radio spectrum (about 3 mc and down) the signal finds an excellent path along the surface of the earth. Although waves travel in straight lines, the conductivity of the ground tends to tilt the wave so that it curves over the horizon. This is

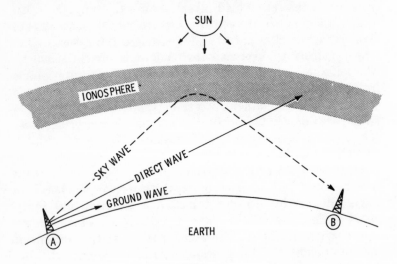

Fig. 3-1. Radio-wave propagation and the ionosphere.

known as *ground-wave* transmission. Since it does not depend on the shifting ionosphere, a ground-wave signal is quite reliable from year to year. Thus, it is widely used for standard broadcast and certain radio-beacon stations, where permanent coverage is important. The chief limitation of the ground wave is range. Although signals follow the earth's curve, they surrender energy to the ground in the process. Only in special applications is it worthwhile to run the enormous power required to propagate the ground wave over more than a few hundred miles. Another serious handicap is the amount of space available in the low-frequency portion of the spectrum. Only a limited number of stations can fit in the few-megacycle spread where ground-wave transmission is favorable.

Ignoring for a moment the 3- to 30-mc region, consider frequencies in the VHF and higher bands. Here, the most significant path is line-of-sight, or *direct* wave. As the wave leaves the antenna, it travels primarily between ground and the ionosphere. Poor earth conductivity at these frequencies makes ground waves virtually nonexistent. Note in Fig. 3-1 that the direct wave penetrates the ionosphere with no apparent change in direction. This is a result of the ionosphere's selective behavior on frequency; as the frequency becomes higher (in megacycles) the ionized layers exert less of a bending influence. This accounts for the straight-line path of high frequencies; they are ultimately lost to space. Reception on VHF and upper bands occurs largely when both transmitting and receiving antennas can "see" each other. Note that a receiver (point B) is too far below the horizon to pick up the direct wave from point A. For reception to occur, B would have to be moved closer to A, or, when practical, have its antenna raised to intercept the wave.

Again we have a radio path which does not largely depend on the ionosphere, is also limited in range, but offers day to day reliability. Services which use direct-wave propagation include TV, FM broadcast, and various short-range and mobile operations. (There are notable exceptions to the range limitation in the over-30-mc region. These are described later in the book.)

There is some short-wave listening via ground- and direct-wave paths, but the vicinity of 3- to 30-mc (HF) forms the heart of the SWL hobby. It is in this third category that the ionosphere produces the skip phenomenon. In Fig. 3-1 the skywave is seen leaving transmitting antenna A and bouncing off the ionosphere. The reflected signal leaves the ionosphere at about the same angle of entry, and receiver B intercepts the energy as the wave returns to earth. It is possible, too, for the wave at B to reflect from the earth's surface and repeat the identical process for a second skip, or *multihop*, transmission. Depending on a variety of conditions, great distances may be covered by a skip path. It is not uncommon for short-wave stations to broadcast to areas situated many thousands of miles distant from the transmitting tower.

Many variables must be taken into account in any attempt to predict the distance covered by the skipwave. One of them is frequency. As mentioned earlier, when the frequency of a signal increases, less ionospheric bending occurs. The principle is shown in Fig. 3-2 where all conditions are comparable, except frequency.

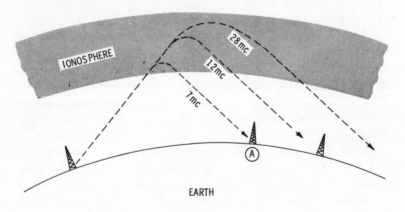

Fig. 3-2. Ionospheric effects on different frequencies.

In Fig. 3-2, the tower is radiating three signals: 7, 12, and 28 mc. Notice that the relatively high 28-mc signal follows a long sweeping arc through the ionosphere as it is bended. In fact, the resulting reflection is not sufficient to bring the signal back to earth; it shoots off into space. If the signal wave were steadily reduced in frequency, increased bending would ultimately bring it back to the earth's surface. This occurs at the *critical* frequency.

The two remaining signals, 7 and 12 mc, are well within the critical limits. They are shown returning to earth after a single skip. Note that 7 mc covers a shorter distance (lower frequency means a sharper angle through the ionosphere). In this example, the 7-mc signal would be called the maximum usable frequency (MUF) for transmitting to point A. It is the highest frequency that can be used to strike that particular location.

For the sake of clarity, the three signals in Fig. 3-2 are shown leaving the transmitting tower at rather high angles. In practical applications, however, long-distance stations generally design their antennas to keep the "angles of fire" as low as possible. When the radio wave is transmitted nearly parallel to the earth's surface, the total distance covered is at its greatest. Also, less bending in the ionosphere is needed to effect a return trip to earth.

The dynamic nature of the ionosphere causes considerable variation in the example. As mentioned earlier, the height of the layers changes with the sun's position. This influence also changes the reflection angles. In winter, for example, the shorter distance between the earth and sun produces greater concentrations of ultraviolet rays on the upper atmosphere. The ionosphere now becomes thick-layered; and its bending effect is more pronounced. One result is that winter can cause a return to earth of signals that are normally lost in space during summer. These are the frequencies which exist above the critical limit in summer, but angle down sufficiently during winter.

Over an average 11-year cycle, sunspots exercise a major influence on critical frequencies. As the number of sunspots

29

rise, solar radiation climbs with it, and the ionosphere deepens. The net result is that during peaks in the sunspot cycle, higher frequencies are usable for long-distance skip. During dips in the cycle, the critical frequency hovers in the low 20- to 30-mc region.

Much of the ionosphere's character is still the subject of intense investigation. There are aspects of its behavior about which little is known. Massive disturbances occasionally occur during *ionospheric storms*, which appear to arise during certain types of sunspot activity. These can absorb signals and virtually wipe out communications over a wide band for days at a time. Fast moving layers, known as *sporadic*-E ionization, appear intermittently in summer and open higher portions of the radio spectrum to an abnormal amount of skipping.

But the variation of the ionosphere is no serious deterrent to the short-wave listener. Aided by the ample frequency coverage of the typical short-wave set as well as the large number of SW stations, some section of the spectrum is always open.

Chapter 4

The Short-Wave Receiver

As the major piece of equipment in the hobby of short-wave listening, it is the receiver's job to convert the minute energy of a radio wave to an audible signal. How well a receiver can do this is mostly a measure of its sensitivity and selectivity. The first quality, sensitivity, is the ability to separate a signal from the ever-present noise level created by disturbances in the atmosphere and outer space.

Selectivity describes how well the receiver can pick out a signal in a crowded frequency band. It is mainly by these two qualities that a short-wave receiver may be judged. A multitude of features may appear in a given set but these are mostly concerned with operating convenience rather than operating quality.

BASIC RECEPTION

The sections shown in Fig. 4-1 make up the fundamental building blocks of the short-wave receiver. The first point encountered by radio waves is the *antenna*. Energy cuts across the wire and creates tiny electrical currents which surge up and down according to frequency. Since all waves in the immediate vicinity cause antenna.currents to flow, it is the job of the tuner to select the desired wave. As the operator moves the receiver tuning dial, the circuit either accepts or rejects the incoming frequency.

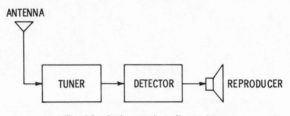

Fig. 4-1. Basic steps in radio receiving.

The signal emerging from the tuner is still radio-frequency energy. It is the job of the *detector* to recover the voice or music, which has travelled atop the radio wave and to present this *intelligence* to the next stage—the reproducer (earphones or speaker). Either of these devices is capable of changing audio frequencies (within the range of hearing) to audible sound waves.

With these basic concepts in mind, we can consider two major receiver types. The simpler of the two contains the regenerative circuit. Although it has certain limitations, it survives today because of few parts and low price. The circuit is illustrated in Fig. 4-2 in block diagram form.

As radio-frequency signals enter the RF amplifier, they are boosted in strength and applied to the regenerative detector. Not only is audio recovered from radio frequency, but an additional effect occurs in this stage; that is, regeneration, which is represented by an arrow marked *feedback*. After the signal passes through the detector, a small portion of it is returned to the entry point. In effect, the stage is given another opportunity to boost, or amplify, the original signal. Audio currents emerge from the detector, and drive the earphone.

32

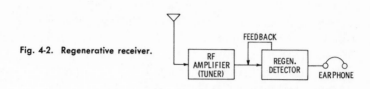

Fig. 4-2. Regenerative receiver.

Due to the feedback principle, the regenerative receiver displays a great deal of sensitivity with simple circuits. Its chief drawback is in the area of selectivity. As a signal be-

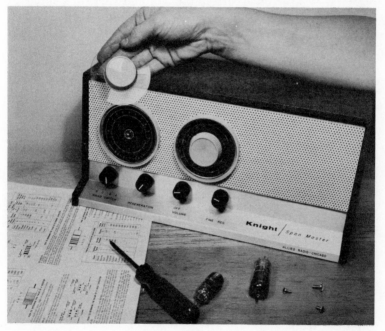

Courtesy Allied Radio Corp.

Fig. 4-3. Knight-Kit Span Master is an inexpensive regenerative set which can be assembled at home.

comes stronger in the regenerative set, it has the tendency to occupy a larger width on the tuning dial—a disadvantage under crowded conditions. It is often difficult, or sometimes

33

impossible, to tune in a weak station that is close in frequency to a relatively strong one. Yet the regenerative circuit remains quite popular today as an inexpensive source for short-wave listening. If the selectivity loss is tolerated, the circuit will bring in a considerable number of distant stations. A typical set is shown in Fig. 4-3.

The *superheterodyne* receiver overcomes the disadvantages of the simpler regenerative set. Through a process of juggling frequency, the superhet can tune sharply to signals of virtually any strength. The operation is shown in Fig. 4-4. Antenna signals are first applied to the RF amplifier, where they are tuned, strengthened, and then presented to the mixer. Both the mixer and local oscillator work together to overcome a disability in circuits operating at high frequencies. It is a general rule that the higher the operating frequency, the greater is the *bandwidth* of the receiver tuning circuits. This simply means that the receiver finds it more difficult to single out one station from a group, if all stations occur high in the band.

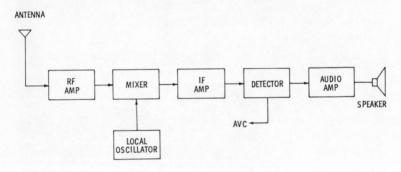

Fig. 4-4. Superheterodyne receiver.

Thus, the set's selectivity is poorer on 30 mc, for example, than on 12 mc. The mixer and local oscillator, however, correct this situation. No matter what the received station frequency, they convert it down to an extremely low value, which is termed the *IF frequency*. To illustrate how it is produced, assume that a short-wave station is transmitting on 12,200 kc (12.2 mc). The signal progresses through the RF amplifier and reaches the mixer; here, it encounters another signal (as shown by the arrow) that is produced by the local oscillator. The oscillator behaves much like a miniature transmitter, generating a flow of radio-frequency current precisely on 12,655 kc. The mixer stage is thereby provided with two signals: the original 12,200 kc from the short-wave station, and the 12,655 kc from the local oscillator.

Both frequencies proceed to mix in the tube; the result is a difference of 455 kc. This is the heterodyne principle, where a mixing together of two signals produces a third frequency. A familiar example of the idea occurs when two adjacent notes on a piano are struck. Not only are the two original tones heard, but a "sour" sound is also created. It is the result of tones mixing, establishing a "beat" note which upsets the normally pleasant sound of the piano. The beat signal in the receiver, however, achieves the desirable result of transforming the original station frequency down to the very low value of 455 kc. In this region, tuning circuits are quite sharp and selective.

How the local oscillator consistently produces the proper mixing frequency is determined by the tuning dial of the receiver. As the operator selects a station, the dial not only varies tuning of the RF amplifier, but controls the local oscillator as well. No matter what the incoming station frequency, the oscillator will *track* to produce a signal 455 kc higher. When the receiver is tuned to 3,000 kc, for example, the oscillator automatically generates 3,455 kc.

Next in the chain is the IF amplifier. This is a stage which accepts the signal (now 455 kc) and boosts its strength. It does this in a highly efficient manner. Unlike the RF amplifier, which must tune over a large range of frequencies, the IF amplifier operates solely on 455 kc. This single-channel nature permits excellent efficiency.

The detector and audio amplifier complete the receiving process as the signal is converted to audio-frequency energy and finally amplified for driving the speaker.

An additional circuit in the superhet receiver, shown as AVC in the diagram, aids in the control of sensitivity. It is entirely possible for an incoming station to overload the RF and IF stages, causing mushy sound in the speaker. This is corrected by the automatic volume control (AVC) at the detector. As the signal grows stronger, the AVC voltage correspondingly increases. When fed back to the RF and IF tubes, it reduces their ability to amplify. Over-all action is smooth and continuous to keep the sensitivity of the receiver within the proper limits. When extremely weak signals occur, AVC virtually disappears, and the circuits are allowed to run wide open.

RECEIVER CONTROLS

The number of knobs, switches, and dials on the front panel of a short-wave receiver is subject to much variation. In Fig. 4-5, for example, an elaborate set with almost a dozen individual elements to be tuned, adjusted, or observed is shown. With some experience, the infinite number of possible dial combinations can help strip a weak signal of noise, thus making it perfectly clear for listening. Consider each major element which might appear on the front panel of a superhet SW receiver (Fig. 4-6).

On the large rectangular dial (Fig. 4-6) there are four major divisions, marked A,B,C, and D. These represent the four bands, encompassing the total frequency coverage of the set. Closer inspection reveals that it starts at 550 kc near A and terminates at 30 mc on band D. This indicates that the receiver is capable of an over-all range of 550 kc to 30 mc, the coverage typical of most SW sets. Band A is devoted to standard AM broadcast, a factor which increases the utility value of the receiver. The first SW band starts at B with 1.6 mc, immediately above the broadcast band. When considering any short-wave receiver, be certain that the bands run continuously with no gaps in the coverage. Many SW-receiver manufacturers make amateur radio receivers which look quite similar in appearance to their short-wave models. If these units are limited to ham bands only, they will not afford the necessary short-wave coverage. Just be certain that each band progresses to the next with an uninterrupted rise in frequency. (There are general-coverage receivers, however, which may be operated on both ham and SW.)

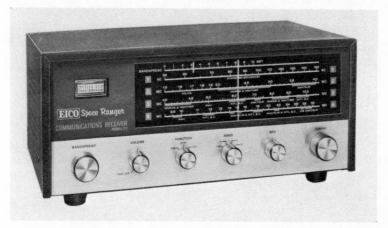

Courtesy EICO Electronic Instrument Co.

Fig. 4-5. The EICO Model 711 short-wave receiver.

The calibration of a typical band is shown on band B. Beginning with 1.6 mc, each division increases the frequency by 0.1 mc (100 kc), a spacing which may not be the same for higher bands.

Assume that you wish to tune in a station on 5,100 kc (5.1 mc). The set is first turned on by moving the function selector from Off to AM. (All SW-broadcast stations transmitting music and voice use AM, or amplitude modulation.) Then, the Band Selector is clicked to the appropriate band, C in this case. Note that there are two tuning knobs to select the frequency, Main Tuning and Bandspread. Before touching the Main-Tuning control, the Bandspread is always preset to one end of its scale, as recommended by the manufacturer. Unless this step is done, the frequency shown on the dial face will not be correct. Now the Main-

Tuning dial is manipulated to bring the large pointer to the division between 5.0 and 5.2 mc. If the desired frequency does not fall exactly on a dial calibration, the operator must do some estimating. For example, on 5,150 kc, the pointer would be centered in the space between 5.1 and 5.2 mc. (Note that 5.1 mc is not marked as such, but represented by a small division on the scale.)

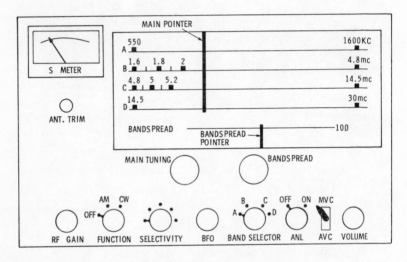

Fig. 4-6. Front-panel receiver controls.

The purpose of the Bandspread dial is to provide a means of fine tuning. It gives the effect of expanding a small portion of a band to make station location easier. Main Tuning, which is quite rapid, is most useful for locating a particular segment of a band, while Bandspread most conveniently picks out a particular frequency. For many SW receivers, the Bandspread scale is marked in arbitrary numbers, not representing actual frequencies, but rather dial-pointer positions. As the Bandspread pointer is moved from 100 toward zero, it lowers the frequency of the receiver by several hundred kilocycles. This affords a second method for station location, as compared with the system just given, where Main Tuning was set directly on 5,150 kc. Main Tuning is left on 5,200 kc and Bandspread slowly rotated toward zero until the desired station on 5,150 kc is heard. For future reference, both Main Tuning and Bandspread numbers may be noted and the station quickly relocated.

The action of the S Meter renders valuable information about signal conditions. As the receiver is tuned, the pin will rise and fall with signal strength. Thus, the meter is a helpful tuning aid. The Bandspread is carefully adjusted until the pin reads highest on a particular station. When conditions are unstable, the pin will swing intermittently downward each time the signal fades. Heavy atmospheric noise also registers on the meter, revealing at a glance the natural noise level in relation to station strength. The S Meter is also useful for giving signal reports to SW stations. The meter face is marked off in universally understood S units and decibels.

Other dials on the front panel allow a range of adjustments for improving reception. The antenna trimmer (ANT. TRIM.) under the S Meter helps to match the antenna to the first tuning circuit in the set. In operation, it is rotated until the S Meter indicates a high reading for a given station. The setting remains the same over a given portion of a band but should be touched up for each station tuned. When ignition or atmospheric noises are high, they can be reduced by the automatic noise limiter (ANL).

Problems of noise and interference are the province of the Selectivity control usually found on the more expensive receiver. It is generally a multiposition switch which adjusts the bandwidth of the receiver from broad to narrow. However, the choice of selectivity is not always a simple one. As the switch is advanced toward the narrow limit, the quality of speaker sound begins to deteriorate. The greatest naturalness in tone, expecially important when receiving music, occurs in the broadest selectivity position. But interference located a few kilocycles from the station frequency can make listening impossible. An increase in selectivity by one or two switch positions can usually reject

39

the interfering signal, if the poorer audio quality is acceptable. This problem is far less important on voice. Since the requirement for voice is intelligibility rather than pleasing tones, the receiver can be narrowed considerably to eliminate interference. Maximum selectivity, however, is not preferred, since higher-voice tones are sliced off and the words become increasingly difficult to understand. The sharpest selectivity is normally reserved for code reception, where signals are extremely narrow. It should be noted that as receiver selectivity is increased, the amount of noise pickup is lessened. Again, the operator must choose the amount of selectivity according to the existing conditions.

The remaining controls are chiefly for code reception and thus are valuable if the SWL'er intends to learn International Morse Code in preparation for a ham radio license. To set up the receiver for this type of reception, the Function Selector is turned to CW (continuous wave). This energizes a circuit in the set which supplies the necessary tone. The BFO (beat-frequency oscillator) control enables the code tone to be varied for the most pleasing sound. Neither the S meter nor the AVC can follow the rapid fluctuations of a code signal. The AVC-MVC switch is placed on MVC (manual-volume control). This disables the meter and brings into play the RF-Gain control. If a CW signal overloads the receiver, RF gain is manually varied to reduce the sensitivity.

The receiver just described is not an actual set, but it does typify the type of equipment the SWL'er is likely to encounter. The placement of knobs and dials is by no means standard; it is apt to vary from one model to the next, yet, their basic functions remain the same. How well the receiver performs is also subject to considerable variation. Two different receivers may have similar controls marked "Selectivity," but this is not a guide to the effectiveness of the circuits behind the panel. As with most electronic equipment, the reputable manufacturer improves circuit quality and performance with price.

Chapter 5

Antennas

Following the receiver, the next most important piece of short-wave equipment is the antenna. It is the job of the "skyhook" to intercept radio waves in the immediate vicinity and convert them into currents to be delivered to the receiver. Most SW sets pick up some distant stations with a short length of wire attached to the antenna terminal. But, the number of signals is surprisingly increased with an efficient antenna high and in the clear.

It is more appropriate to consider an antenna as a system comprising three elements: antenna, transmission line (popularly called the lead-in), and ground (Fig. 5-1). The antenna proper is the section which performs the actual

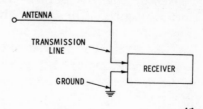

Fig. 5-1. Elements of an antenna
system.

signal pickup. To this end, it is mounted as high as possible. Be certain that it is free of nearby obstructions which may block the waves. Coupled into the antenna is the transmission line for carrying the signal down to the receiver's antenna terminals. The remaining element is the ground which helps to complete the signal pathway and affords some degree of protection from lightning. Practical short-wave antennas often combine one or more of these elements; for example, antenna and transmission line may be a single, uninterrupted run of wire.

In selecting from among the various antenna types, the SWL'er must compromise in antenna length. Any piece of wire behaves like a tuned circuit to radio waves; as it is made shorter, it tends to favor higher frequencies. Thus, a dilemma develops in the attempt to choose a single length to operate efficiently over the wide frequency spectrum of the short-wave bands. An antenna on 3 mc, for example, performs best with a length of about 150 feet, while a 15-foot wire best serves 30 mc. It is impractical to erect a multitude of antennas to cover all frequency groups, but there are workable techniques. With the high sensitivity of today's short-wave receiver, a single compromise antenna, the inverted L is quite adequate for most listening. As the SWL'er advances in his hobby, he may resort to a more specialized antenna (detailed later) to improve sensitivity in a particular band or groups of bands.

INVERTED L

This is the simplest and most common SW antenna, deriving its name from a resemblance to the letter L placed upside down (Fig. 5-2A).

Over-all length of the wire is 40 to 100 feet with no distinct transmission line other than the antenna wire itself. Depending on available space, the antenna should run as long and straight as possible to the far support.

Consider a step-by-step procedure for installing an inverted L. It is best to begin by figuring out the most con-

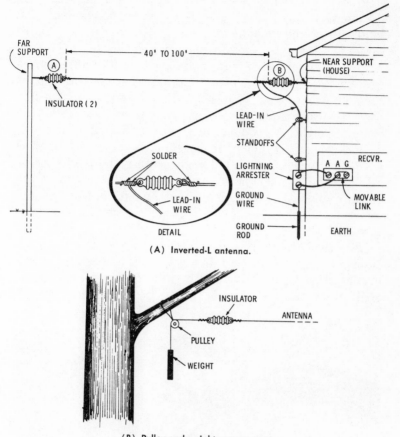

(A) Inverted-L antenna.

(B) Pulley and weight arrangement.

Fig. 5-2. Details of an antenna system.

venient location for the far support. This may be a nearby pole, house, or garage roof. A tree is a definite possibility if certain requirements are fulfilled. First, it must be fairly rigid; sway is liable to snap the wire. Try to select a tree with a relatively thick trunk; it is feasible to use a thin tree, but some method of allowing for movement must be devised. The system shown in Fig. 5-2B is one suggestion. In any case the far support should permit maximum antenna height—30 feet or more off the ground, if possible.

43

Next, determine the distance from far to near supports plus the length required for the lead-in part of the antenna. The total will be the amount of wire needed for the job. Don't forget to allow extra footage for inside the house.

Almost any type of wire can serve for the antenna, as long as it will not sag over a period of time. The heat of summer can cause considerable wire-length expansion. Also, the formation of ice in the winter can lower the original height. A good choice of wire is No. 12 or 14 hard-drawn copper, as shown in Fig. 5-3. It does not matter whether the wire is coated with enamel or other kind of insulation. The only place bare metal must show is at the hookup point at the receiver's antenna terminals and the solder points shown. (Another good wire choice is copper-clad steel.)

The installation job is made easier if most assembly work is done before the antenna is erected. While on the ground, insulators at points A and B may be fastened to the ends of the antenna wire (Fig. 5-2). The insulators may be por-

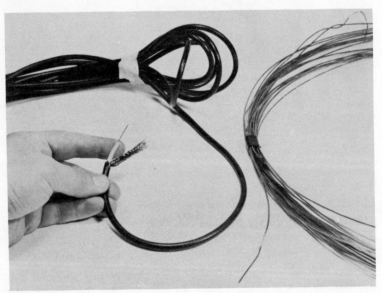

Fig. 5-3. Large roll of wire is hard-drawn copper, and the other is coaxial cable.

celain or glass of the 3- or 4-inch size (Fig. 5-4). Solder the lead-in section of the wire and bring it down the side of the house through insulated stand-offs. The screw-in type used for TV twin lead can serve equally well in this case. The antenna loses least signal if it is not permitted to come in contact with any surface as it runs down the side of the

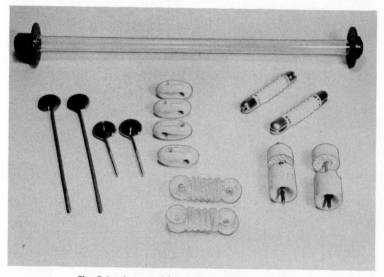

Fig. 5-4. Suggested hardware for stringing antenna.

house—this also includes the entry point. (A lightning arrester, Fig. 5-5, is recommended at the entry point.)

When the antenna is actually raised, extreme caution must be observed. The wire should never be allowed to touch, or even pass close to, power lines. Not only is this in the interest of safety, but noise interference generated by the line is reduced. Final attachment of the insulators to the far and near supports may be done with appropriate lengths of the same wire used for the antenna.

A good ground is essential for the lightning arrester to properly drain off electrical charges which occur during a thunderstorm. (A direct hit by lightning is not necessary to cause sparking and possible damage to the tuning section of the receiver.) The ground system consists of heavy bare wire run to a pipe driven into the earth. (Both of these items are commonly available where TV parts are sold.) The same ground may be used to hook the receiver's G terminal to earth.

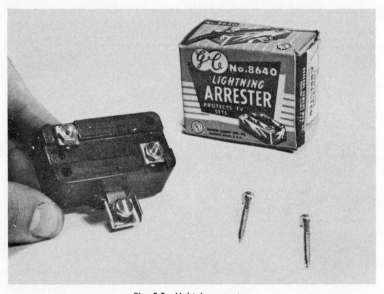

Fig. 5-5. Lightning arrester.

In the case of the apartment dweller, the ground system outlined may be impractical. The alternative is to use the electrical ground of the building. This may be at a cold-water pipe or the screw that holds the cover plate on an AC wall outlet. (In no instance should a gas pipe serve as a ground.) Special grounding clamps (Fig. 5-6) are sold for providing good contact with a pipe.

An important consideration while grounding occurs in the case of the AC-DC short-wave set. It could be hazardous to ground any of the screws used to hold the cabinet or chassis in place. Just be certain to follow the manufacturer's recommendations, which usually indicate that only the terminal marked G or GND be used for grounding.

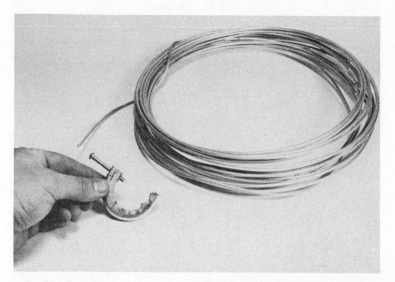

Fig. 5-6. Special clamp and heavy aluminum wire recommended for ground leads.

The completed inverted L antenna displays some directionality; that is, it favors signals arriving from certain directions. Since different frequencies react to antenna length in varying manners, it is difficult to predict the pattern of response. Generally, the antenna tends to favor those signals which arrive broadside to its length. Thus, signals from east and west might be heard more strongly in an antenna which lies in a north-south direction. The directional problem is not usually serious, but some experimentation might prove worthwhile. If space permits, a new far support might be located and the direction of the antenna changed for improved results.

The other two antennas to be described are of interest to the more advanced listener who is willing to sacrifice the broad response of the inverted L in favor of improved performance on a narrower range of frequencies. The same basic constructional techniques apply as before. Maximum height assures good signal pickup and a reduction in noise from man-made sources, such as motors, power lines, and automobile ignition.

FOLDED DIPOLE

Chiefly for single-band operation, this antenna is constructed with TV-type twin-lead wire rated at 300 ohms

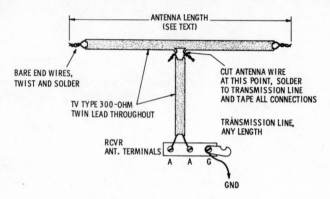

Fig. 5-7. Folded-dipole antenna.

(Fig. 5-7). The length of the top part of the wire determines the operating frequency. (The lead-in or transmission-line section may be any length in all cases.) Finding the correct length for any particular frequency is done with the aid of a simple formula:

$$\text{Length in feet} = \frac{468}{\text{frequency in mc.}}$$

To illustrate the use of the formula, assume you wanted to cut the antenna for the 31-meter band, which extends from 9,200 to 9,700 kc. First, the center of the band, which is 9,450 kc, is converted to megacycles, or 9.45 mc. Inserted into the formula:

$$\text{Length in feet} = \frac{468}{9.45}$$

The answer is approximately 49 feet. This is the dimension indicated as antenna length in Fig. 5-7. The transmission line is joined to the exact center of this length, as shown.

A folded dipole of this size will work well over the complete 31-meter band. It is quite directional and should be oriented so its broadside, or long length, is run at right angles to the stations you wish to favor. Thus, an SWL'er in Chicago might run a folded dipole along a north-south line and achieve greatest sensitivity to stations from Europe to the east and the Orient to the west.

The folded dipole nets a specific advantage over the inverted L. Since the twin-lead running from the antenna to the receiver is a true transmission line, it has the ability to cancel some of the noise originating below the antenna proper. This is not true of the inverted L, which is indiscriminately sensitive over its total length. But again, it should be emphasized that the folded dipole is rather restricted for signals outside the band for which it is cut.

Connecting the folded dipole to the receiver differs from the method of attaching the inverted L. As shown in Fig. 5-2A, there are three terminals on the typical SW receiver —two marked A, and one marked G. For the inverted L connection, a movable link is fastened across A and G and the wire is hooked as illustrated. With the folded dipole, there are two leads from the transmission line and these go to A and A (Fig. 5-7). There's a simple trick for converting the folded dipole to a single-wire antenna that resembles the inverted L in performance. The two wires at the bottom end of the twin lead are twisted together and hooked to the receiver terminals in the same fashion as pictured in Fig. 5-2A.

FAN DIPOLE

Although it is physically the most complex of the three antennas described here, the fan dipole is capable of good response over an approximate range of 6 to 18 mc. It requires about a 30-foot-high support and a transmission line of 52-ohm coaxial line. The dimensions are given in Fig. 5-8. In order to perform well, the shield of the coaxial cable should be properly grounded at the base of the antenna where the leads merge. If the soil is normally moist, a simple ground rod driven to a depth of about 4 feet will

49

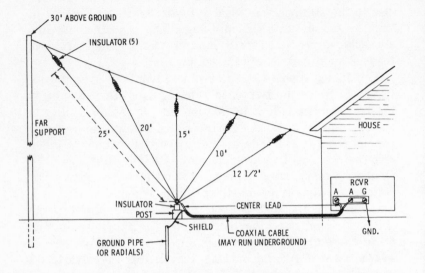

Fig. 5-8 Fan-dipole for multiband use.

suffice. In sandy areas where earth conductivity is likely to be poor, four or five lengths of bare copper wire should be buried in the ground and attached to the coaxial shield. These wires (called radials) can lie a few inches below ground and extend outward from the antenna base in different directions. The fan dipole is a vertical antenna and picks up signals with fairly equal sensitivity in all directions.

Chapter 6

How To Set Up and Operate Your Set

A short-wave receiver may be operated virtually any-where—on a kitchen tabletop or in an elaborate fully-equipped "shack." However, several considerations should be taken into account before choosing a particular location. You'll need room for the addition of accessories, wall space for charts, and a drawer or shelf for various papers.

The neatest installation can be made by placing the receiver near the window where the antenna enters and close to an AC outlet. Such a position reduces the number of trailing wires and aids the antenna by keeping the transmission line short. If this area happens to be in a living room, where other members of the family tend to congregate, remember that they may not be as fascinated as you are with short-wave listening—they may even find sounds from the speaker objectionable or in conflict with a nearby TV set. This problem can generally be eliminated by using earphones. With most SW receivers, the plugging in of earphones automatically quiets the speaker. But there is a disadvantage; earphone listening can become tiring after a while. The earphones are most valuable during late night-listening hours when sounds from the set are apt to be objectionable anywhere in the house.

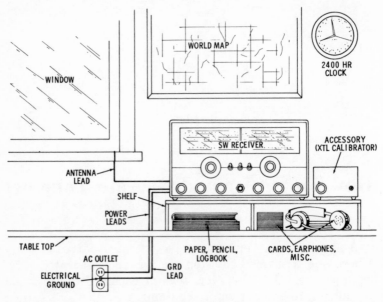

Fig. 6-1. Typical SW setup.

A basic SW setup is shown in Fig. 6-1. Notice that the receiver is not placed directly on top of the table; instead it rests on a shallow shelf. Two purposes are served by the shelf: it is easier to operate controls on the receiver if they are raised several inches above the surface of the table; and the dial face is closer to eye level so that the small numbers and divisions are easier to read. The best receiver position is one in which the top edge of the cabinet is slightly tilted away from the eye. This places the dial directly in line of vision. It provides the same effect as bending your head down to the dial and looking directly at it. These considerations may seem minor at first, but they do pay off handsomely over hours of operating.

52

The supporting shelf for the receiver makes a fine receptacle (or "cubby hole") for storing such assorted necessities as blank paper, schedules, cards and log books. As shown in the illustration, the shelf is extended to the right to accommodate those accessories which the SWL may wish to acquire. The wall above the operating table has ample room for charts of the world and a 2400-hour clock.

CALIBRATION

Although it is possible to search across the SW bands and discover interesting stations by accident, it is a definite advantage to know how to calibrate the dial accurately. Most short-wave dials are simply not accurate enough to be used as an absolute guide to frequency. Some kind of dependable reference signal is necessary to correct for error or unmarked frequency divisions. Whichever method you choose, the receiver should be permitted to warm up for at least a half hour in advance. This allows all circuits to reach proper operating temperature and cuts down the amount of drifting. Otherwise you are liable to calibrate the receiver and find that readings have shifted due to heating. That extra half hour of operation need not alarm anyone about the cost of electricity. A typical SW set, operated on the average AC line, may be run five hours on a penny! As far as wearing out the set, there is no problem here, either. If the ventilation holes on the cabinet are not blocked from air circulation there are no harmful effects. (Most receiver wear actually occurs because of the surge of electricity when the set is turned on.)

One simple method of calibration is with known stations. After some experience is gained on the bands, certain strong stations are readily located. If their announced frequencies are noted, it is a simple matter to use them for future reference. Assume that a known station is on 9120 kc, but your dial incorrectly indicates 9240 kc when that station is tuned in. The dial error therefore is +120 kc. This error will probably hold true for several hundred kilocycles above and below the known frequency. Thus, if you wished to find a station on 8870 kc, you would first set the dial pointer on this frequency and then move it *down* 120 kc to allow for the error. It is possible to "spot" comparable points in other bands with several known stations for other calibration markers.

Of great value to the SWL'er is the service provided by the National Bureau of Standards, a branch of the U.S. Government. This agency operates powerful stations in Colorado and Hawaii which transmit signals of extremely high accuracy throughout the spectrum. Not only do they provide calibration points, but time signals as well. These stations are readily identified by the sound of a tone and ticking, plus voice announcements according to the schedule given in Table 6-1.

The most efficient means available to the SWL'er for pinpointing frequency is the crystal calibrator. This is an accessory which generates a series of accurate and closely spaced signals through the complete range of the SW receiver. These signals are heard as a tone when the BFO, or CW oscillator, on the receiver is turned on. The device is available in a transistorized version which needs no power source other than its own internal battery. On the lower

Table 6-1. Standard frequency stations and propagation reports.

Station	Freq. in Mc	Location
WWV*	2.5, 5, 10, 15, 20, 25	Fort Collins, Colorado
WWVH*	5, 10, 15	Hawaii
CHU	3.330, 7.335, 14.76	Ottawa, Canada
JJY	2.5, 4, 5, 8, 10, 15	Tokyo, Japan

* Propagation Reports Broadcast as Follows:
For North Atlantic Area—WWV, 19½ and 49½ minutes after the hour.
For North Pacific Area—WWVH, 9 and 39 minutes after the hour.
Code Letter W (• – –) = Disturbance Either in Progress or Expected
     U (• • –) = Unstable Conditions
     N (– •) = No Warning
Code Letter followed by number which gives quality of report:
1. (• – – – –) Impossible   6. (– • • • •) Fair to Good
2. (• • – – –) Very poor   7. (– – • • •) Good
3. (• • • – –) Poor   8. (– – – • •) Very Good
4. (• • • • –) Fair to Poor   9. (– – – – •) Excellent
5. (• • • • •) Fair

bands, the calibrator radiates enough signal so that no connection into the receiver is required. For higher ranges, a connection to the antenna terminal may be needed.

The SWL'er is confronted with two basic calibrator types; the 100-kc, or the 100-kc and 1-mc unit. The first calibrator contains a single crystal which produces an accurate signal every 100 kc on the receiver dial up to about 50 mc. The disadvantage of the unit is that some confusion might occur in a receiver that is considerably off calibration. The second version takes care of this problem. In addition to 100-kc signals, it generates a second series of marker signals that are spaced at 1-mc intervals along the dial. Thus, the 1-mc position is used to locate the nearest whole megacycle number on the band and the 100 kc marker for narrowing the calibration more finely. The typical unit illustrated in Fig. 6-2 also contains a trimmer adjustment for zeroing its crystals precisely to the accurate signals transmitted by the frequency-standard stations.

TIME CONVERSION

Many short-wave schedules are conveniently printed in the listener's local time. For example, an SWL'er on the west coast of the U.S.A. might note that a program from Radio Sweden will be aired at 8:00 a.m., Pacific Standard Time (PST). No calculations are required—the listener simply looks at his own clock and tunes in at the appointed hour. Of course, it is not 8 a.m. in Sweden at the time of the broadcast. To prevent confusion over the different time zones throughout the world, a standard system has been universally adopted. It is GMT, or Greenwich Mean Time. In many instances a program schedule is expressed entirely in GMT and requires that the listener figure out what it means in terms of local time. Converting GMT to local time is not a difficult calculation and should be a permanent part of the SWL'er's basic technique.

The idea behind GMT is the use of a single point in the world which stations and listeners alike agree on as a reference. Down through the years, the Greenwich observa-

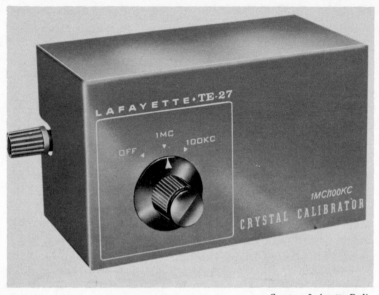

Fig. 6-2. Crystal calibrator, 100 kc and 1 mc.

tory, located at the south coast of England, has served this purpose. Another aspect of GMT is that time is based on a 2400-hour clock, as opposed to the more familiar 12-hour type. This further prevents confusion by eliminating the possibility of 8 o'clock meaning either a morning or evening hour. Table 6-2 gives the 24-hour equivalents of local time. Note that 2030 hours, for example, would mean 8:30 P.M.

Let's assume a schedule states that a program is to be aired at 1300 GMT. If you consult Table 6-3, it will be seen that various time zones in the U.S.A. lag behind GMT by a certain number of hours. For those located on the east coast, the number "–5 hours" applies. This means that you should deduct 5 hours from GMT; the answer is local time for that area. Thus, a program aired at 1300 GMT will be picked up at 0800 EST, or 8 o'clock in the morning. Let's say a listener in the midwest wishes to hear a program scheduled for 0200 GMT. Applying the "–6 hours" shown

Table 6-2. Local time versus 2400-clock time.

Conventional Clock	2400-Hour Clock
12 Midnight	0000
1 AM	0100
2 AM	0200
3 AM	0300
4 AM	0400
5 AM	0500
6 AM	0600
7 AM	0700
8 AM	0800
9 AM	0900
10 AM	1000
11 AM	1100
12 Noon	1200
1 PM	1300
2 PM	1400
3 PM	1500
4 PM	1600
5 PM	1700
6 PM	1800
7 PM	1900
8 PM	2000
9 PM	2100
10 PM	2200
11 PM	2300

for the Central Standard Time Zone, the answer is 2000 hours local (or CST) time. This is 8 o'clock in the evening.

A handy accessory which automatically figures out these time relationships is the 2400-hour clock. The model shown in Fig. 6-3 tells GMT and local time (anywhere in the world) at a glance.

Assume that the clock is used in the vicinity of New York City and that local time is 15 minutes past 11 in the evening. The hour hand, as illustrated, points nearly straight up at 23 (2300 hours) and the minute hand is on the 15

Table 6-3. Converting GMT to local time*.

Local Time	GMT	Local Time	GMT
Atlantic Standard Time	−4	Yukon Standard Time	− 9
Eastern Standard Time	−5	Alaska Standard Time	−10
Central Standard Time	−6	Bering Standard Time	−11
Mountain Standard Time	−7	Hawaii Standard Time	−10
Pacific Standard Time	−8		

* Add 1 hour to final answer for Daylight Saving Time.

Fig. 6-3. A 2400-hour clock.

minute mark at the right. Notice the light-colored disc on the
clock; this is actually a map of the world projected from
the South Pole. To find GMT, it is only necessary to find
"London-GMT" printed on the edge of the disc and read
the time indicated at this point. In this example, it is just
above the minute hand and occupies the 0400 position
(shown as "4"). Thus, 2315 EST (New York time) is the
same as 0415 GMT. The whole map rotates continuously
with the minute hand and all time zones shift simultane-
ously. The time in other world locations on the map may
also be checked with this system.

The only precaution in using the chart in Table 6-3, or
the clock just described, occurs in the areas of the U.S.A.
which use Daylight Saving time during the summer months.

Since all the figures are true for standard time only, a 1-hour adjustment must be made. Always add an hour to the final figure whenever calculations are made in a Daylight Saving time period. (The same precaution applies when using receivers which have built in devices for calculating time, as shown in Fig. 6-4.)

These are the basic tools of the SWL'er. Handling of receiver controls is best learned by actual experience rather than through a detailed description given here. However, there are two general recommendations in operating technique which should prove a distinct advantage. Most importantly, tuning should be done gingerly and with extreme

Courtesy Zenith Electric Co.

Fig. 6-4. Transoceanic portable has built-in time-determining device.

care. The short-wave bands are often quite crowded and hasty dial twisting can cause you to overlook much of the interesting material being broadcast. Finally, don't hesitate to freely experiment with different control settings. A change in selectivity here, or a touch up of the antenna trimmer there, will often salvage what sounds like a hopelessly weak station and render it perfectly readable.

All short-wave listening is by no means restricted to the elaborate setup just described. With the emergence of the transistor, portables similar to the one shown in **Fig.** 6-5 enable the hobbyist to carry on his activities anywhere. Re-

Courtesy Heath Co.

Fig. 6-5. The Heath *Mohican* general coverage receiver.

quiring little battery power, these sets have coverage on the major SW bands and perform well under favorable conditions. The model illustrated in Fig. 6-5 has a 10-transistor circuit that operates on standard flashlight batteries for approximately 400 hours. This portable may also serve as a first ham receiver. Although frequency coverage is continuous through all short-wave bands, major ham bands are directly calibrated on the bandspread tuning dial.

Chapter 7

Chasing DX

Listening to the world's short-wave stations requires some electronic detective work. It is true that some activity always prevails on the bands, but much of the choice listening results after careful preparation. There are program schedules to be studied, propagation reports to be analyzed, and logs written up and consulted. These are the tactics needed to unearth DX (the general term applied to distant stations). Chasing DX presents an interesting challenge to the SWL'er, especially in the face of changing conditions.

SHORT-WAVE BROADCAST BANDS

Periodically, most countries of the world meet at an international convention to decide which bands are to be set aside for short-wave broadcasting. These frequencies, as shown in Table 7-1, fall within the coverage of the typical receiver. While short-wave listening is not restricted solely to this part of the spectrum, it remains the chief hunting ground for DX.

Table 7-1. International short-wave broadcast bands.

Meters	Frequency Range
60	4750 kc to 5060 kc
49	5950 kc to 6200 kc
41	7100 kc to 7300 kc
31	9200 kc to 9700 kc
25	11700 kc to 11975 kc
19	15100 kc to 15450 kc
16	17700 kc to 17900 kc
13	21450 kc to 21750 kc

60-Meter Band

This is primarily a domestic band; that is, the stations are broadcasting to local listeners. However, it is often possible to receive such signals at considerable distances. The 60-meter region is designated the "tropical band" since many of the stations are situated in South and Central America. Occasionally, the central and southern parts of Africa are also heard.

Reception on the band is usually most favorable during winter months in the early evening.

31-, 41-, and 49-Meter Bands

These three bands are grouped together since they perform in a similar manner and are populated by the greatest number of international stations. Here will be found most of the powerful stations from all over the world. The frequencies are open during many hours of the day and evening and provide the richest source of DX for the listener. Signals tend to be strongest during the evening in winter on 49 and 41 meters, while the 31-meter band often holds up well in the evening hours throughout the year.

13-, 16-, 19-, and 25-Meter Bands

Located in the upper reaches of the radio spectrum, signals on these bands are significantly subject to changes in sunspot activity and season. The general rule states that as the number of sunspots increase, the higher frequencies are received over longer distances. The 13-, 16-, and 19-meter

Table 7-2. A schedule of station and frequencies.

Frequency in kc	Call Sign	Location
3955	Radio Vaticana	Vatican City
4770	ELWA	Monrovia, Liberia
4780	YVLA	Valencia, Venezuela
4805	ZYS8	Manaus, Brazil
4893	Radio Senegal	Dakar, Senegal
4910	HCIMI	Quito, Ecuador
4920	VLM4	Brisbane, Australia
4940	—	Abidjan, Ivory Coast
5033	—	Lobito, Angola
5960	HJCF	Bogota, Colombia
5985	4VB7	Port Au Prince, Haiti
5985	—	Hilversum, Netherlands
5990	—	Havana, Cuba
6005	RIAS	W. Berlin, Germany
6025	—	Lisbon, Portugal
6030	—	Baghdad, Iraq
6040	VOA	Los Angeles, U.S.A.
6050	BBC	London, England
6055	JOZ2	Tokyo, Japan
6060	YDF	Djarkarta, Indonesia
6070	BBC	London, England
6080	ZL7	Wellington, New Zealand
6080	—	Tangiers, Morocco
6090	VL16	Sydney, Australia
6090	—	Junglinster, Luxembourg
6100	—	Belgrade, Yugoslavia
6105	—	Moscow, U.S.S.R.
6110	BBC	London, England
6145	RTF	Allouis, France
6170	VOA	Tangiers, Morocco
7105	—	Madrid, Spain
7150	—	Moscow, U.S.S.R.
7165	RFE	Munich, Germany
7193	—	Bucharest, Rumania
7250	BBC	London, England
7265	—	Saigon, Vietnam (Rep.)
7290	RAI	Rome, Italy
7480	—	Peking, China
9009	—	Tel Aviv, Israel
9410	BBC	London, England
9505	NHK	Tokyo, Japan
9520	—	Copenhagen, Denmark
9530	AIR	Delhi, India
9535	HER4	Berne, Switzerland
9610	—	Oslo, Norway
9660	LRX	Buenos Aires, Argentina
9700	—	Leopoldville, Congo Rep.
9735	—	Cologne, Germany
10910	—	Ulan Bator, Outer Mongolia
11685	Radio Vaticana	Vatican City
11720	—	Brussels, Belgium
11745	—	Cairo, Egypt
11770	VOA	Munich, Germany
11780	NHK	Tokyo, Japan

63

Table 7-2. (Continued)

Frequency in kc	Call Sign	Location
11830	—	Montevideo, Uruguay
11840	—	Lisbon, Portugal
11845	—	Karachi, Pakistan
11850	—	Sofia, Bulgaria
11855	DZH8	Manila, Philippines
11865	PRA8	Recife, Brazil
11890	BBC	London, England
11900	CE1190	Valparaiso, Chile
11950	—	Mecca, Saudi Arabia
11990	—	Prague, Czechoslovakia
15080	—	Melbourne, Australia
15410	—	Peking, China
15160	—	Ankara, Turkey
15165	—	Damascus, Syria
15190	—	Helsinki, Finland
15215	Radio Vaticana	Vatican City
15225	—	Tapei, Taiwan
15230	—	Prague, Czechoslovakia
15235	NHK	Tokyo, Japan
15280	ZL4	Wellington, New Zealand
15345	—	Rabat, Morocco
17705	—	Luanda, Angola
17780	BBC	London, England
17890	HCJB	Quito, Ecuador

bands are usually heard during daylight hours with some nighttime listening possible during the summer. All bands in this region are unstable in that rapid changes in conditions are common.

A representative schedule of stations and frequencies heard on the North American continent is given in Table 7-2. The frequencies shown are not necessarily constant; in some cases, stations shift channels according to propagation conditions.

AMATEUR BANDS

The ham bands are liberally sprinkled throughout the short-wave dial. Many hum with activity as U.S. hams contact each other and their counterparts in other countries. Their ensuing conversations are often technical in nature—signal reports are exchanged, equipment and antennas discussed, and comments given on band conditions. There is, however, plenty of general "rag-chewing" which makes for interesting listening, especially when equipment is taken into the field (Fig. 7-1). Hams often volunteer for emergency communications during disaster. Note the whip antenna on the vehicle at right in Fig. 7-2.

The behavior of the ham frequencies follows that of the

Courtesy QST Magazine.

Fig. 7-1. Hams operating under field conditions.

conditions described earlier for the SW bands. The 160- and 80-meter bands, for example, are restricted to fairly short-range communications of several-hundred miles. Long-haul contacts, extending to many thousands of miles, are usually made on the 40- and 20-meter bands. Higher frequencies also skip considerable distances but are more susceptible to solar activity. The major bands of interest are shown in Table 7-3.

In most instances, a portion of each ham band is used for CW, or code use. This affords an excellent opportunity for code practice by the SWL'er who wishes to acquire a

Fig. 7-2. Vehicle at right can be used by hams for emergency messages.

Table 7-3. Ham bands found on conventional SW receiver.

Meters	Frequency in kc
160	1800 - 2000
* 80	3500 - 4000
** 40	7000 - 7300
20	14000 - 14350
15	21000 - 21450
10	28000 - 29700
*Novice CW - 3700 - 3750	
**Novice CW - 7175 - 7200	

ham license. Careful tuning will provide transmissions at virtually all code speeds. A steady source of slow-speed signals at approximately five words per minute is found on the two Novice CW bands of 80 and 40 meters.

CITIZENS BAND

Toward the end of the 1950's, the Federal Communications Commission removed the 11-meter band from ham use and reassigned it to a newly created section of the Citizens Radio Service. Popularly known as Citizens Band (CB), the band is used for short-range business and personal communications with low-power equipment. The range of CB signals is usually less than 20 miles from the transmitting point, but the great number of stations on the air provide the SLW'er with signals in nearly all parts of the country. CB stations are not permitted to make long-distance contact via skip, but the phenomenon does occur on the 27-mc frequency allocated to the service. It is not uncommon to hear two CB stations located a thousand or so miles away from the SWL'er talking to each other.

The channels in this service are listed in Table 7-4. These frequencies are labeled on most SW sets, but may be marked "11-meters" or "amateur band" on older models.

Table 7-4. Location of Citizens band.

Channel	Frequency in kc
1	26965
2	26975
3	26985
4	27005
5	27015
6	27025
7	27035
8	27055
9	27065
10	27075
11	27085
12	27105
13	27115
14	27125
15	27135
16	27155
17	27165
18	27175
19	27185
20	27205
21	27215
22	27225
23	27255

MARITIME MOBILE BAND

If you wish to tune in on traffic concerned with activity on the water, the spot to find is 2 to 3 mc located near the low end of the dial. This is where the tugboat captains, private and commercial boats, and the Coast Guard conduct much of their communications. There is ship-to-ship and ship-to-shore activity of many types. Of course, the strongest signals are heard when the SW set is located near large bodies of water found on the East, West, and Gulf Coasts and the Great Lakes area. However, signals do travel considerable distances inland. Much of the interesting activity is from pleasure boat owners. During summer weekends, the marine band is filled with such talk as where the fish are biting. The single most important channel in the band is 2182 kc. This is the calling and distress frequency monitored by the Coast Guard on a continuous basis.

An important function in the marine band is the broadcasting of weather reports by both commercial and Coast Guard stations. The schedules shown in Table 7-5 give a detailed listing of coastal stations and when they may be heard.

A second marine band exists at frequencies in the VHF region which is not included on general-coverage short-wave receivers. Monitoring VHF marine broadcasts requires a special-coverage receiver, as mentioned in a later section. There are approximately two dozen channels assigned in the 156-157 mc region for communications between boats and shore stations. The significant frequency in the band is 156.8 mc, a channel which is continuously monitored by the U. S. Coast Guard for possible distress calls. The range of stations operating in this band is limited to about 20 to 30 miles. Thus, any monitoring must be within a reasonable distance of boating or shipping areas.

FREQUENCY-STANDARD STATIONS

Dotted throughout the bands are the frequency-standard stations. As described in the preceding chapter, they provide special services to anyone who wishes to use them. With extreme accuracy, time signals, reference tones, and propagation reports are transmitted. It should be possible to pick up at least one of the channels at any given time, since transmitting power is high.

VHF SPECTRUM

The use of two-way radio has increased tremendously over the past years and daily the spectrum grows more crowded.

Table 7-5. Location of marine stations broadcasting weather reports.

Location	Call Sign	Frequency in kc	Local Time
Boston, Mass.	WOU	2450,2506	0520,1720 2320
New York, N. Y.	WOX	2522,2590	0715,0915
Ocean Gate, N. J.	WAQ	2558	0715,0915
New Castle, Del.	—	2558	0730,1930
Baltimore, Md.	—	2558	0745,1945
Norfolk, Va.	WGB	2538	0600,1800 1200,2400
Charleston, S. C.	WJO	2566	0715,0915
Jacksonville, Fla.	WNJ	2566	0700,1900
Miami, Fla.	WDR	2490	0715,0915
Tampa, Fla.	WFA	2550	0700,1900
New Orleans, La.	WAK	2482,2598	0800,2300
Galveston, Texas	KQP	2530	1230,1900
San Pedro, Calif.	KLH	2506,2450	0830,2030
Eureka, Calif.	KOE	2506,2450	0900,2100
Astoria, Oregon	KFX	2598	0915,2115
Portland, Oregon	KQX	2598	0930,2130
Seattle, Wash.	KOW	2522	0900,2100
(Following are U.S. Coast Guard Stations. Emergency broadcasts made immediately.)			
Boston, Mass.	NMF	2694	1120,2320
New York, N. Y.	NMY	2662	1150,2350
Cape May, N. J.	NMK	2662	1250,0050
Norfolk, Va.	NMN	2702	1220,0020
Charleston, S. C.	NMB	2678	1120,2320
Jacksonville, Fla.	NMV	2678	0120,1320
Miami, Fla.	NMA	2678	1150,2350
St. Petersburg, Fla.	NOF	2678	1120,2320
New Orleans, La.	NMG	2686	1150,2350
Galveston, Texas	NOY	2686	1120,2320
Long Beach, Calif.	NMQ	2694	0900,2100
San Francisco, Calif.	NMC	2662	0830,2030
Seattle, Wash.	NMW	2702	0930,2130

The situation has assumed such distressing proportions that many of the services the SWL'er wishes to hear are no longer found within the range of basic SW receiver coverage from .5 to 30 mc. Of particular interest, for example, are the activities of local police and fire departments. In a move to alleviate crowded conditions, the Federal Communications Commission (FCC) has shifted most of these frequencies into the more spacious VHF band (30 mc to 300 mc) where the line-of-sight path keeps them fairly short range. This practice allows the same frequency to be assigned to many areas of the country without undue interference.

However, the SWL'er still has access to VHF frequencies if he is willing to purchase the necessary receiving equipment. The receivers are generally available in three separate models to cover the most popular VHF bands.

Some are dual-band models, which cover two of the major bands. Another method for receiving VHF is to add a converter to a conventional AM radio or short-wave receiver. As its name implies, a converter is an accessory which converts the VHF signal down to a frequency which can be picked up on a conventional AM or short-wave receiver. Converters are usually restricted to a small portion of any given band (often a 1-mc segment). For this reason, it is advisable to learn in advance which frequency or channels you wish to monitor before ordering the converter. In many instances, you must inform the converter manufacturer of the desired frequency since a suitable receiving crystal must be factory installed. The three major VHF bands are divided into these frequency groupings:

30-50 mc Medium range police communications, radio paging systems, mobile telephone, industrial communications, and other services.

108-135 mc Aircraft in flight and aircraft control towers. (Note: Other aircraft frequencies are covered on HF (3-30 mc), especially for long-range flights.)

150-174 mc Police, fire departments, marine emergency

70

*(150-174 mc services, mobile telephone, taxicabs, trucks, and
  cont.)   others.*

Notice that there is some overlap in assigning certain services in more than one band. Table 7-6 shows a complete
chart of the various categories and frequencies on VHF.

If you are unable to find out the frequency of the local
police or fire department, there is a way of approximating
it, at least to the degree of discovering the band to which
it is assigned. The method relies on the fact that the whip

Table 7-6. Services on VHF (30 mc to 300 mc).

Frequency Allocation (mc)	Services
	30 — 50 mc BAND
30.56 - 32	Industrial, land transportation, public safety
33 - 34	Public safety, industrial
35 - 36	Industrial, maritime mobile, domestic public, land transportation
37 - 38	Public safety, industrial
39 - 40	Public safety
40 - 42	Industrial, scientific and medical equipment
42 - 50	Public safety, industrial, maritime mobile, domestic public, land transportation.
	108 — 135 mc BAND
108 - 118	Aeronautical radionavigation
118 - 132	Aeronautical mobile control towers, private aircraft, commercial aircraft, flight tests and schools, utility.
	150 — 174 mc BAND
150 - 174	(Same services as under 30 - 50 mc band, plus following.)
157.1	Government
157.2	Government

Classification

Aeronautical—Commercial and private aircraft, ground stations.
Industrial—Power, petroleum, forest products, news services, motion
      picture studios, businesses, construction, farming.
Land Transportation—Common and contract carriers of freight and passen-
      gers; railroad, taxi, motor carrier, auto emergency.
Public Safety—Police, fire, forestry, highway maintenance, disaster relief,
      physicians in rural areas, ambulance, rescue.
Marine—Commercial and private stations in maritime activities.

antenna is cut to the operating frequency. (As discussed in the chapter on antennas, a given frequency operates best with a discrete antenna length.) First step is to judge the length, in feet, of the whip as closely as possible. Then divide its footage into 234. The answer reveals the approximate frequency in megacycles. For example, if the whip appears to be about six feet in height, the frequency is roughly 39 mc (234 divided by 6). This places it within the 30-50-mc band. On higher bands whips are far shorter, but still adhere to the same formula. (The method is based on the fact that mobile whips are customarily designed to be one-quarter the physical length of the radio wave.)

VERY LOW-FREQUENCY SPECTRUM

The very-low-frequency (VLF) band, along with VHF, is not included on the conventional short-wave set. Occupying the space below the standard AM broadcasting band, the channels are principally assigned to radio-range beacon stations. The only reason for mentioning the band is that VLF coverage is sometimes found on the two- and three-band transistor portables marketed for the small boat owner. These sets usually have movable loop antennas which enable the operator to "home in" on the VLF signal for radio direction finding.

Another useful aspect of the band is that it provides a steady source of weather information. The listing given in Table 7-7 comprises stations which operate on a 24-hour daily schedule and transmit weather reports every 15 and 45 minutes after the hour.

LOGS AND RECORDINGS

The pleasure of short-wave listening is enhanced by keeping an up-to-date log. It's a handy record, usually in the form of a notebook, in which information is noted for future reference. Stations heard, comments about program-

(YEAR)						
STATION	LOCATION	TIME	FREQUENCY	DATE	RECEPTION QUALITY	REMARKS

Fig. 7-3.   Headings for radio log.

ming, times, frequencies—all may be charted as suggested
in Fig. 7-3. Not only is it interesting to reread months later,
but it serves a practical purpose as well. A detailed log will
contain current information on operating schedules and frequencies announced over the air. It is fine for recounting
to friends and family the fascinating DX picked up during
the wee hours of the morning.

A tape recorder is another handy accessory for recre-
ating for others the exciting events heard on the bands. If
one is readily available, it is a simple matter to record
broadcasts off the air. Use the setup shown in Fig. 7-4. A
pair of wires is clipped to the speaker lugs of the short-wave
receiver and terminated at the input of the tape recorder.
(Use the "phono" or "tuner" input on the machine.) With
this system, the normal sound from the set is undisturbed.
If you hear hum in the recording, reverse the two clip leads
to the speaker lugs.

QSL CARDS

Collecting colorful verification reports from SW stations
is a highly prized activity among short-wave listeners.
Known as QSL cards, they are sent out by stations to listeners who wish to verify the fact that the signal was received. Tacked up on the wall, as pictured in Fig. 7-5, they

Table 7-7. VLF stations; weather information broadcast every 15 minutes and 45 minutes after the hour, 24 hours a day.

Location	Call Time	Frequency in kc
East Coast		
Bangor, Maine	BGR	239
Portland, Maine	PWM	215
Boston, Mass.	BOS	382
Squantum, Mass.	SQT	233
Providence, R. I.	PVD	347
Providence, R. I.	NCO	356
New York, N. Y.	LGA	209
Hempstead, N. Y.	HEM	227
Newark, N. J.	EWR	379
Millville, N. J.	MIV	365
Atlantic City, N. J.	NBB	212
Chincoteaque, Va.	NKZ	221
Norfolk, Va.	NGU	269
Norfolk, Va.	ORF	281
Elizabeth City, N. C.	NTU	356
Myrtle Beach, S. C.	MYR	203
Charleston, S. C.	CHS	329
Savannah, Ga.	SAV	263
Jacksonville, Fla.	JAX	344
Daytona Beach, Fla.	DAB	284
Melbourne, Fla	MLB	257
W. Palm Beach, Fla.	PBI	365
Gulf Coast		
Key West, Fla.	FMY	341
Tampa, Fla.	TPA	388
Cross City, Fla.	CTY	269
Pensacola, Fla.	PNS	326
New Orleans, La.	MSY	338
Beaumont, Texas	BPT	368
Galveston, Texas	GLS	206
Palaciaos, Texas	PSX	350
Corpus Christi, Texas	CRP	382
Pacific Coast		
San Diego, Calif.	SAN	224
Oceanside, Calif.	OCN	323
Long Beach, Calif.	LGB	233
Los Angeles, Calif.	LAX	332
Camarillo, Calif.	CAV	359
Santa Barbara, Calif.	SBA	350
Farallon Is., Calif.	F	314
San Francisco, Calif.	SFO	227
Arcata, Calif.	ACV	209
Astoria, Oregon	AST	323
Hoquiam, Wash.	HQM	254
Neah Bay, Wash.	EBY	391
Whidbey Is., Wash.	NUW	353
Bellingham, Wash.	BLI	362

make an interesting display gleaned from all parts of the world.

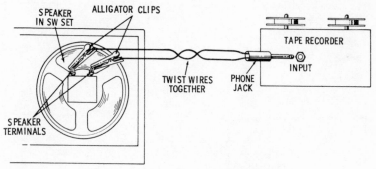

Fig. 7-4. Tape recording short-wave messages.

To obtain QSL's, the short-wave listener should prepare a brief but detailed report of conditions which existed at the time the signal was received. Accuracy is important; the information is of technical value to the stations in checking their coverage area. As shown in Fig. 7-6, stations are interested in gathering reports and data on radio propagation.

Your report, in card or letter form, should contain the following information:

1. The exact time (local or GMT) of reception.
2. Date of reception.
3. Frequency.
4. Program identification.

   This may be the name of the program or a word description. Include subject matter, titles of musical selections, or other identifying features.

5. Radio conditions.

   Describe reception in terms of strength: strong, good, fair, poor, or unusable. Was interference absent, slight, moderate, severe, or extreme? What was the nature of the interference—code, other station, static, or fading?

6. Receiving equipment.

   Name your receiver and antenna type.

7. Request QSL card or verification report.

Fig. 7-5. Colorful QSL cards from SW stations make
an interesting display.

In the case of international broadcast stations, return
postage is not always required. However, the greatest response occurs if you include an International Reply Cou-
pon with all requests, especially for nonbroadcast services.
Such coupons are available at your local post office and may

be exchanged by the station to whom you send them for
postage. Remember, do not send stamps for return postage,

Fig. 7-6.   Engineer at SW station charts frequencies and band
conditions to help improve reception.

since U.S. stamps will not be valid in the country to which you send the letter.

OTHER AIDS

An excellent publication for the SWL'er is inexpensively available from the U.S. Government Printing Office. It is a booklet which gives an over-all listing of radio-frequency allocations agreed on by international treaty. Covering the spectrum from 10 kc to over 30 mc, it shows which segments are assigned to various broadcast and communications services. A copy may be secured by writing to: Superintendent of Documents, U.S. Government Printing Office, Washington, D.C. 20402. Ask for Vol. 2 of FCC Rules and Regulations. Cost of the volume at the time of this writing is $2.00. It will also contain information about other radio services which are not necessarily of interest to the SWL'er. It is not possible, however, to separately order the section which pertains to frequencies (Part 2).

From the same address, you can secure "Broadcasting Stations of the World," a publication of the U.S. Information Agency, priced at $1.50.

The U.S. Government also makes available predictions of radio conditions by the National Bureau of Standards. The reports are mailed monthly for the yearly charge of $1.00. Request "Central Radio Propagation Laboratory Bulletin; National Bureau of Standards." The address again is that of the U.S. Government Printing Office.

Other publications and current reports of SW activities are found in the pages of the various electronics magazines sold on the newsstands.

Chapter 8

Signals From Space

A new era in short-wave listening was introduced with the launchings of space vehicles. Equipped with miniature transmitting equipment, orbiting satellites were soon discovered to emit radio signals which could be picked up on home-type equipment. The field has grown to provide new challenges for the DX hunter who wishes to expand his horizons to outer space. Unlike casual tuning on the conventional bands, monitoring spacecraft calls for new skills and knowledge on the part of the hobbyist.

Most of the current listening is concerned with identifying the source of assorted beeps, clicks, and rushing sounds which make up space-vehicle transmissions. The signal is usually a complex one, comprised of data channels which send the various measurements sensed by the craft back to earth. It is usually beyond the capability of the SWL'er to interpret the composition of the signal (AM, FM, CW, etc.) ; however, the actual monitoring of the signal provides the reward.

Another aspect of space communications is the supporting network of ground stations. They often transmit on frequencies within the coverage of a conventional SW receiver. It is especially interesting to listen to these ground stations during manned space flights. Signals via skip from ground stations permit monitoring of such activities as launch preparations and recovery.

The principal requirement for tuning satellites is tuning the equipment on the proper band. Table 8-1 gives a listing of frequencies used for space and related activities. Of course, this chart is not permanent, and is subject to change in the future. Some satellites burn up in the atmosphere after a period of transmitting; others are purposely quieted by ground-control stations. However, the listing serves as an approximate guide to those portions of the radio spectrum which have been utilized for several years. It will be seen that frequencies in the 8-, 15-, and 20-mc regions fall directly into the range of most SW receivers. Others require VHF equipment that is capable of pickup at much higher frequencies. One popular approach is the use of a converter. This is a device which is attached to the antenna terminals of the conventional short-wave set and converts the received signal from VHF to HF. Whatever the system, a crystal calibrator is indispensable. The low power of spacecraft transmitters, often a few thousandths of a watt, means tuning must be "on the nose."

In the area of antennas, good results have been achieved with simple, single wire setups discussed earlier. Emphasis should be on length; the longer the antenna the broader its pickup pattern tends to be. After some experience is acquired, the SWL'er may wish to experiment with high-gain directional antennas precisely cut for the exact frequency of reception. However, it should be noted that most spacecraft are constantly in motion and create tracking problems with the highly directional antennas.

Some of the communications satellites (for example, Early Bird), however, are in synchronous orbit, which means they apparently hover at a fixed point. Although these

80

Table 8-1. Space frequencies.

Frequency in mc	Space Vehicle	Remarks
8.9	— — —	This approximate frequency is commonly used in recovery operations for manned space vehicles.
15.061	— — —	This frequency and its immediate vicinity are commonly used for ground communications in support of U.S. manned space vehicles.
19.895	— — —	This frequency is used for voice and code communications between Soviet ground stations and that country's manned space vehicles. Vicinity of 20 mc also used by Soviet for many of its unmanned orbiting vehicles.
40.01	Explorer 27	
136-137	— — —	This VHF band is one of the most active for U.S. satellites. Some examples follow:
136.14	Relay 1	
136.232	Tiros 9	
136.41	Pegasus 2	
136.44	Early Bird	
136.47	Syncom 3	
145	OSCAR	On this approximate frequency in the 2-meter band is a series of ham-radio satellites constructed by hams and launched by NASA. OSCAR means "Orbiting Satellite Carrying Amateur Radio."

satellites would provide choice listening, this is not yet practical for the home hobbyist. To achieve synchronous orbit, the satellite must be more than 22,000 miles high. This calls for an extremely sophisticated antenna system. In addition, the signals are transmitted in the microwave region (millions of megacycles) and suitable receiving equipment is now impractical for the SWL hobbyist.

Telemetry signals from orbiting satellites are literally snared on the run. As a vehicle circles the earth, reception time is a few minutes' duration in any given region. Best results occur if the receiver is warmed up and on frequency just prior to an expected "pass" over your region. This information can be secured from published reports in newspapers and scientific magazines. Look to these sources, too, for timely information on frequencies. On the regular shortwave bands, it is often announced by Radio Moscow for Soviet space activities. Information on U. S. space flights is sometimes available from the Office of Public Information, NASA, 1512 H Street, Washington, D.C.

Once you're certain that the receiver is properly calibrated, and the satellite is due to appear shortly, the BFO is turned on. (This is the same control used for code reception.) This signal mixes with the incoming satellite carrier within the receiver to produce an audible tone. The most characteristic feature of the sound is that it changes in pitch due to the Doppler Effect. As illustrated in Fig. 8-1,

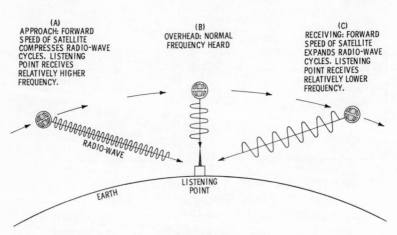

Fig. 8-1. Doppler effect on radio wave from space causes tone change at listening point.

an approaching spacecraft is emitting a radio carrier on a fixed frequency. However, the forward movement of the craft *adds* to the speed of the transmitted radio wave. The effect is that of compressing cycles together and raising the total number which occur each second. Thus, the receiver on the ground picks up energy which is slightly higher in frequency than the actual wave at the satellite's antenna. As the vehicle passes overhead, or achieves the "point of closest approach," the true frequency is received. Under this condition, forward speed is not adding as before. The opposite result occurs when the signal moves away from the listening point. Movement of the receding satellite now subtracts from the speed of the wave as it travels back toward the receiving point.

What the listener hears during these phases when the satellite is "acquired" is a rising tone on the approach that is followed by a lowering of the tone after it passes by. The basic effect is identical to the familiar example of a passing railroad train. The rise and fall in the pitch of the whistle may also be explained by the Doppler Effect on sound waves.

The apparent shift in satellite frequency is not very great, often on the order of several thousand cycles. With the receiver tuned to the exact center frequency of the satellite transmitter, the resulting tone in the speaker changes over a band within the range of human hearing. Again, it should be noted that other sounds may be superimposed on the satellite signal. Many forms of intelligence are impressed on the basic carrier which represent telemetering data.

Chapter 9

Hints on Maintaining Your SW Set

With the passage of time, the SW receiver may experience a gradual or sudden deterioration in performance. Many of the problems can be solved only by a competent serviceman and expensive test equipment. However, there are simpler problems which the SWL'er may correct.

Any steps which require removal of the chassis from its cabinet should be approached with caution. Voltages in the circuits usually run as high as 250 volts and could cause dangerous shock. The line cord must always be removed completely from the AC outlet before any work is done in this area. Unless you have the skill and equipment, none of the tuning screws inside the cabinet should be touched. Rarely will these adjustments get out of alignment.

NOISE

Many troubles give the effect of originating inside the receiver, but are actually generated externally. The principal problem of this type is man-made electrical noise. It arises from the operation of motors, household appliances, TV sets, automobiles, and other devices which cause either sparking or a sudden change in the flow of electrical current. In the majority of cases, noise appears directly on radio frequencies and rides into the receiver through the antenna or power line.

A simple test is to disconnect the antenna from the set. If noise drops, it is an indication that it is entering via the antenna. This should not be confused with the normal atmospheric level which produces a steady hiss at all times. What you are listening for is a quieting of clicks, buzzes, and other sounds which occur during those intervals when the noise-generating device is at work. The sparking of an oil burner, vacuum cleaner, electric shaver, or pump, for example, are intermittent in nature.

There are two approaches to curing noise induced into the antenna. The first is height; the higher the wire, the less susceptible it becomes to noise pickup. Man-made interference tends to occur at or near the ground. In bad cases, converting to a coaxial cable transmission line (see Chapter 5) is another technique. The shielded braid of the cable is immune to noise energy between the receiver and antenna proper. Another measure is to avoid the use of vertical antennas which are more sensitive to noise pickup than the horizontal wire.

Yet another plan of attack is to reduce noise pickup by filtering at the offending source. This is impractical for passing automobiles, but useful for appliances in the home. One effective technique is the addition of bypass capacitors within the case of the appliance; a job often reserved for the serviceman. One noise offender frequently overlooked is the fluorescent lamp. It is a prolific generator of 60-cycle "hash" due to the rapid ionization of gas in the tube. Much of it can be suppressed by following the bypass technique given in Fig. 9-1. A .01 mfd disc capacitor (rated at 600 working volts minimum) is soldered across the AC wires as close to the fixture as possible. Be careful to tape all ex-

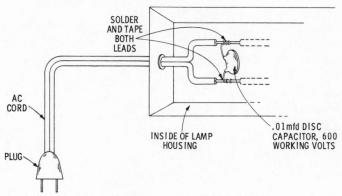

Fig. 9-1. Bypassing radio noise from fluorescent lamp.

posed wires to prevent short circuits. Another bypassing measure utilizes two of these capacitors, as shown in Fig. 9-2. It works if the metal case of the fixture is at electrical ground. This will be true if the fixture is a permanent type mounted on the ceiling, as opposed to the desk-lamp models.

The identical procedure can be followed for other devices, if you can gain convenient access into the case. Typical units would be an electirc fan, machine tool, washing machine, etc. Just be sure to connect any bypass capacitors to incoming AC wires and avoid other leads in the appliance.

Besides radiation through the air, noise may gain entry to the receiver through its AC power cord. Try reversing the line cord in the wall socket. If this does not improve conditions, a means of bypassing must be employed. Although receivers generally contain a bypass capacitor internally, it may not be effective for shunting higher noise frequencies to ground. There's no reason to remove it, but it is a good idea to add two ceramic disc capacitors (rated at .01 mfd, 600 working volts), as shown in Fig. 9-3. These units are most effective when positioned as close as possible to the point of entry of the line cord. If there is no convenient mounting point, add a terminal strip under the chassis as shown.

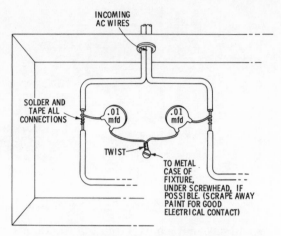

Fig. 9-2. Another method of bypassing radio noise in
permanent-type fluorescent fixture.

Tougher cases of interference brought in by the line cord
require more elaborate treatment. There are line-cord fil-
ters, commercially available for a few dollars, which
contain both capacitors and radio-frequency chokes for sup-
pressing line noise. To function properly, they must be provided with a good electrical ground (discussed earlier).

Many noise sources transmit energy in both major pat-
terns, through the air to the antenna and via the power line.
Thus, a combination of suppression techniques must often
be employed, as in the case of "ITV", or interference from
television. TV sets contain a horizontal oscillator which is
a vigorous producer of harmonic energy over much of the
SW spectrum. This interference is heard as a harsh buzz
that pops in and out as the SW tuning dial is rotated. If the
measures already described do not cut the interference, one
possibility is to relocate the SW set in another room. With
TV sets and fluorescent lamps, additional distance from the
SW receiver often reduces noise considerably.

If the receiver has a noise limiter, it can do much to
minimize all types of sharp, pulse-type interference, especially from auto ignition systems. In spite of this, the preceding noise-reducing measures are worth the effort. Since

88

the noise limiter may introduce some amount of distortion into the sound at the speaker it should be reserved primarily for use when noise is extremely severe.

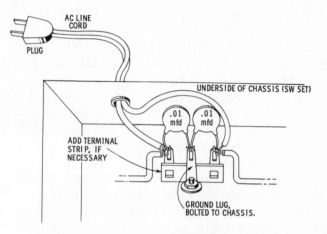

Fig. 9-3. Bypassing radio noise picked up from power line.

INTERNAL PROBLEMS

Now a look at some common defects which occur in the circuitry of a receiver and what to do before seeking professional help.

Tubes

As in any piece of electronic equipment, tubes are responsible for well over half of the troubles. Since defective tubes can cause virtually every known symptom—like hum, distortion, or a totally dead set—they should be checked first. The principal cause of a tube defect is an open filament. If your set is designed for AC operation only, the defect is often apparent; the tube won't light and feels cool to the touch. In AC-DC sets, the failure of *any* tube removes power to all tubes and pilot lamp, necessitating a complete check. Less obvious faults show up only by substituting with a known good tube or testing on a high-quality tube checker (of the mutual conductance type). Tests of

89

this type uncover such problems as partial shorts between elements which cause hum and small changes in tube characteristics that produce a loss of sensitivity.

One elusive problem concerns the local-oscillator tube; it may test good but cause the receiver to malfunction. The symptom to note is good receiver performance on low bands with failure on the higher frequencies. Another sign is that some atmospheric noise is heard on the higher bands, though no signals are received.

Aging tubes may perform well, but produce a ringing sound in the speaker. This is a microphonic condition where loose tube elements are set into mechanical movement when the speaker vibrates or other physical disturbance reaches the chassis.

A profusion of ruggedly-constructed tube types of superior performance is available to use in place of existing ones in the set. In replacing tubes, follow this rule-of-thumb: it is satisfactory to use a new tube which has more numbers and letters than the old one. For example, an old 5U4G may be replaced with a newer 5U4GA or 5U4GB. But, don't reverse the process—that is, using a tube with less numbers or letters than on the original.

Tuning Capacitors

Dirt, grease, and corrosion take their toll at the tuning capacitor. This is the component with two or three moving-plate sections driven by the main tuning dial. A similar but smaller capacitor is used for the bandspread. Signs of trouble in this area include: a scratching sound while tuning on any band, no signals at some points in the tuning range, or a completely dead receiver. Careful cleaning of these variable capacitors often cures the problem. This may be done by blowing air between the plates, then brushing with a radio-type solvent. One important area is at the wiper contacts of the capacitor bearing. Finally, check for tightness of the capacitor-mounting screws. Sometimes these screws pass through rubber shock absorbers which can cause microphonics if they have hardened with age.

90

Controls and Contacts

As one of the frequently used parts in the set, the volume control is subject to damaging wear. The earliest sign is a scratching sound as the knob is rotated. When the condition worsens, noise might occur with no movement of the control. A technique which greatly extends the life of the part is the injection of liquid contact cleaner. Introduce it into the small spaces between the lugs on the control while rotating the knob rapidly back and forth.

The same treatment may be given other mechanical components which acccumulate dust and dirt. Also apply contact cleaner to all switches and controls.

Another troublesome area is the space between lugs on all tube sockets. Foreign matter accumulates here and sets up an electrical path which affects receiver performance. With a soft brush dipped in the liquid contact cleaner go over every visible socket space and flush it clean.

AC Cord

The greatest point of stress on the power cord is where it meets the AC plug. Any sign of cracking or fraying of the insulation here should be corrected before a short circuit or shock hazard occurs. Replacing the cord completely can be done with conventional lamp-type wire, except in the case of some older AC-DC sets. (These models sometimes have a resistance wire built into the cord and must be renewed with an identical replacement part.)

Dial Cord

Slippage of a pointer is traced to the dial cord. If the problem is slight, a special dial-cord dressing usually corrects the condition. More pronounced cases yield to a small amount of tightening of the spring which holds one end of the cord to a tuning drum. If the cord is broken or stretched beyond adjustment, it should be replaced—but never without the stringing diagram. Otherwise, hours will be spent in trying to figure out the loops and circles the cord is supposed to follow.

OTHER PROBLEMS

Speakers develop defects which cause distortion in sound reproduction. Gently touch the center of the paper cone with a fingertip and push it in a fraction of an inch. If you feel any rubbing, the speaker is ready for replacement. Small tears in the paper cone may be repaired with clear cement. Cabinets, dial windows, speaker grilles, and other parts loosen with age and should be retightened periodically. Mounted securely, they are less likely to produce hard-to-trace noise of a mechanical or electrical nature.

Index

Station (cont'd)
  French, 11
  ham, 13, 15
  Japanese, 12
Stations, maritime, location
    of, 69, 74
Steel wire, copper-clad, 44
Storms, ionospheric, 30
Sunspots, 26, 29-30
Superheterodyne receiver, 34
Switch, AVC-MVC, 40

T

Time conversion, 55-59
Tracking, oscillator, 35
Transmitter, 17-20
  French, 18
Transmission
  ground-wave, 27
  multihop, 28
Transoceanic portable, 59
Trimmer, antenna, 39
Tube problems, 90
Tuning capacitor problems, 90-91
Twin lead, TV, 45

U

Ultraviolet radiation, 25-26

V

Very low frequency
    spectrum, 72, 74
VHF
  spectrum, 68-72
  range, 23-24
Volume control
  automatic, 36
  manual, 40

W

Wave
  cycle of, 20
  direct, 27
  line-of-sight, 27
Wavelength, 17, 21-23
Weather broadcasts, 69, 74
Wire
  copper-clad steel, 44
  hard-drawn copper, 44